THE ROYAL HORTICULTURAL SOCIETY
ADDRESS BOOK

Commentary by Brent Elliott

Illustrations from the Royal Horticultural Society's Lindley Library

FRANCES LINCOLN

Frances Lincoln Limited
4 Torriano Mews
Torriano Avenue
London NW5 2RZ
www.franceslincoln.com

The Royal Horticultural Society Address Book
Copyright © Frances Lincoln Limited 2004

Text and illustrations copyright © the Royal Horticultural Society 2004
and printed under licence granted by the Royal Horticultural Society, Registered Charity number 222879.
Profits from the sale of this address book are an important contribution to the funds raised by the
Royal Horticultural Society. For more information visit our website or call 0845 130 4646.

An interest in gardening is all you need to enjoy being a member of the RHS.

Website: www.rhs.org.uk

British Library cataloguing-in-publication data
A catalogue record for this book is available from the British Library

ISBN 0-7112-2394-7

Printed in China
First Frances Lincoln edition 2004

FRONT COVER
A watercolour drawing (1810) of *Callistephus chinensis* and *Coreopsis tinctoria*

BACK COVER
A watercolour drawing (1837) of the snake's-head fritillary, *Fritillaria meleagris*

TITLE PAGE
A watercolour drawing (1835) of a group of *Alstroemeria pelegrina*, *Nemophila menziesii* and *Oxalis versicolor*

OVERLEAF, RIGHT
A watercolour drawing (1832) of *Senecio elegans* and *Trollius europaeus*

INTRODUCTION

During the eighteenth and nineteenth centuries, drawing was considered a suitable skill for a woman to acquire. Few women achieved fame as botanical artists within their lifetimes, but a handful of names show that it was possible: for example, Mary Lawrance, who published books of rose and passionflower portraits at the end of the eighteenth century; and Priscilla Bury, whose *Hexandrian Plants* (1831–4) is a masterpiece of the genre. Far more drew flowers as a hobby. Of those discovered and published in recent times, the best known is Edith Holden, whose nature notes for 1906 were published as *The Country Diary of an Edwardian Lady* in 1977; more recently, Richard Mabey's *Flowers of May* and Todd Gray's *Victorian Wild Flowers of Devon* have brought unknown artists to light. The work of many more no doubt lurks in family papers, boxes or attics, or even library cupboards.

Some time in the late nineteenth or early twentieth century – the exact year is unknown – William Wilks, the Secretary of the Royal Horticultural Society, was offered three volumes of drawings by three different vendors. The drawings were all by the same artist and were in chronological order, the first volume ran from 1808 to 1825, the second from 1832 to 1842, the third from 1842 to 1852. Wilks paid £6 and £8 respectively for the second two volumes; it is not known what he paid for the first. And so more than 300 drawings by Caroline Maria Applebee entered the Society's collection.

Biographical research has yielded little information. Caroline Maria Applebee was born in London in the late eighteenth century, and died in London in 1854. It seems likely that she was upper middle class, because of the number of greenhouse and conservatory plants she drew: it was not until the middle of the nineteenth century, after taxes on glass, bricks and wood were abolished, that ownership of a greenhouse became widespread. She seems to have lived, or at least spent time, in Essex: one of the binders of the volumes was a Colchester firm.

Applebee's earliest drawings must have been made while she was still virtually a child. Her handling of details such as leaf venation improved as she became more experienced, but her skills at composition were apparent from the beginning. The horticultural fashions of the day can be traced in her work: her first volume contains drawings of tulips, and the second ranunculus; in the final volume the florist's calceolaria appears. She also drew wild flowers from the fields and hedgerows. This work, and that of other female painters who documented their local flora, may help current studies of local biodiversity by providing a standard for comparison with the flora of the present.

The three volumes do not cover the years 1825–32. Was there originally another volume? If so, where is it today? Perhaps it is hiding in *your* family papers.

Brent Elliott
The Royal Horticultural Society

USEFUL ADDRESSES AND TELEPHONE NUMBERS

A watercolour drawing (1828) of a daylily, *Hemerocallis fulva*

A

A watercolour drawing (1815) of filberts, *Corylus avellana*

B

A watercolour drawing (1834) of *Magnolia hypoleuca*

B

B

B

A watercolour drawing (1837) of the snake's-head fritillary, *Fritillaria meleagris*

C

A watercolour drawing (1826) of fruits (raspberries, gooseberries, red and white currants)

C

C

C

A watercolour drawing (1810) of the Chinese lantern, *Physalis alkekengi*

D

A watercolour drawing (1838) of *Gaillardia pulchella*, an American annual

D

D

D

A watercolour drawing (1809) of *Dahlia pinnata*, one of the first dahlia introductions

E

A watercolour drawing (1841) of the lily-of-the-valley, *Convallaria majalis*

E

E

E

A watercolour drawing (1830) of *Anemone pavonina* and *Gentiana acaulis*

F

A watercolour drawing (1822) of a wallflower, *Erysimum* (formerly *Cheiranthus*) *cheiri*, and a stock, *Matthiola incana*

F

F

F

A watercolour drawing (1843) of a Japanese iris

G

A watercolour drawing (1847) of early petunia hybrids, *Petunia integrifolia* x *nyctaginiflora*

G

G

G

A watercolour drawing (1849) of *Fuchsia denticulata* (known to Caroline Maria Applebee as *Fuchsia serratifolia*)

H

A watercolour drawing (1850) of *Mahonia aquifolium*, an American shrub introduced in 1823

H

H

A watercolour drawing (1824) of a hollyhock, *Alcea rosea*

A watercolour drawing (1848) of myrtle, *Myrtus communis*, and a hybrid verbena

A watercolour drawing (1847) of *Hebe speciosa*, introduced from New Zealand a decade before the drawing was made

J

A watercolour drawing (1839) of *Convolvulus tricolor*, a Mediterranean bindweed cultivated since the seventeenth century

J

A watercolour drawing (1815) of three tulips, 'The Claude', 'Duke of Sutherland' and 'Duchess of Montrose'

K

A watercolour drawing (1847) of *Camellia* 'Donckelaeri'

K

A watercolour drawing (1846) of the holm oak, *Quercus ilex*, and the Kermes oak, *Quercus coccifera*

L

A watercolour drawing (1843) of *Ranunculus asiaticus* and *Dianthus caryophyllus*

L

L

A watercolour drawing (1835) of *Malope trifida*, a Mediterranean herb introduced in 1808

M

A watercolour drawing (1833) of *Gladiolus psittacinus* (now *Gladiolus dalenii*),
introduced from South Africa in the mid-eighteenth century

M

M

M

A watercolour drawing (1845) of the guelder rose, *Viburnum opulus*

N

A watercolour drawing (1846) of an unnamed chrysanthemum variety

A watercolour drawing (1848) of *Iris pseudacorus* and *Carex pendula*

A watercolour drawing (1824) of a French marigold, *Tagetes patula*

A watercolour drawing (1832) of the small bindweed, *Convolvulus arvensis*

P Q

A watercolour drawing (1831) of a moss rose, *Rosa x centifolia* 'Muscosa'

P Q

R

A watercolour drawing (1847) of a group of *Nemophila menziesii*, *Ceanothus azureus* and *Nemophila atro-purpurea*,
North American plants introduced in the early nineteenth century

R

A watercolour drawing (1834) of forms of *Dianthus chinensis*, the Chinese or Indian pink

S

A watercolour drawing (1820) of *Ranunculus asiaticus* and *Papaver orientale*

S

S

A watercolour drawing (1824) of two tulips, 'The Claude' and 'Duke of Sutherland'

T

A watercolour drawing (1833) of the heartsease or wild pansy, *Viola tricolor*

T

A watercolour drawing (1835) of *Crocus aureus* and *Crocus pulchellus*

A watercolour drawing (1820) of a group of *Daphne cneorum, Jasminum nudiflorum, Omphalodes verna* and *Dicentra eximia*

U V

A watercolour drawing (1841) of the Christmas rose, *Helleborus niger*

W

A watercolour drawing (1833) of varieties of common holly, *Ilex aquifolium*

W

A watercolour drawing (1846) of mistletoe, cypress and cotoneaster

X Y Z

A watercolour drawing (1835) of *Hippeastrum vittatum*, a South American bulbous plant

X Y Z